NUMBER MANIA

NUMBER MANIA
Math puzzles for smart kids

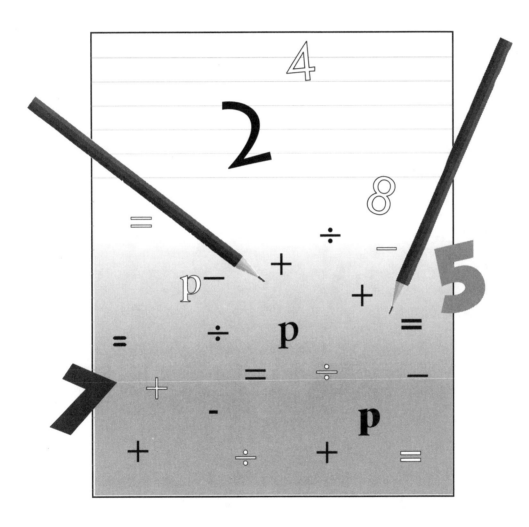

EDWARD GODWIN

Sterling Publishing Co., Inc.
New York

1 3 5 7 9 10 8 6 4 2

Published in 2002 by Sterling Publishing Company, Inc.
387 Park Avenue South, New York, N.Y. 10016
Originally published in Great Britain by Arcturus Publishing Limited
for Index Books in 2000 under the title *Maths Magic*
© by Arcturus Publishing
Distributed in Canada by Sterling Publishing
C/o Canadian Manda Group, One Atlantic Avenue, Suite 105
Toronto, Ontario, Canada M6K 3E7

Sterling ISBN ISBN 0-8069-9359-6

CONTENTS

INTRODUCTION

No matter what your age, *Number Mania* has puzzles that will challenge you. The puzzles in *Number Mania* vary greatly so there is something for children of all ages and abilities.

Number Mania is divided into five challenging tests, where Test 1 is the easiest and Test 5 is the most demanding. However, there is a range of difficulties within each test—so some of the puzzles will seem very easy, while others will take a bit more thought. Many of the more challenging puzzles have a hint to help you, and the answers to each puzzle are given at the back, with a short explanation.

The grids and shapes that make up the puzzles are the same in each test, so you will soon become familiar with them. However, to make each test more difficult, the numbers and the methods needed to solve the puzzles (i.e., subtraction, division, etc.) will be different at each stage.

Start with Test 1 and work through it puzzle by puzzle. Take your time with each puzzle; look hard to see how each one might be solved. Think about adding the numbers up, dividing them, or subtracting them; look for patterns in the numbers—are they square numbers (2 × 2, 3 × 3), cube numbers (2 × 2 × 2, 3 × 3 × 3), or prime numbers (numbers that can only be divided by themselves or 1). Feel your confidence grow as you get the answers right, then move on to the next test. Before you know it, you'll be on Test 5 and won't have even looked at the answers!

ODD ONE OUT

Which number is the odd one out in each oval?

1

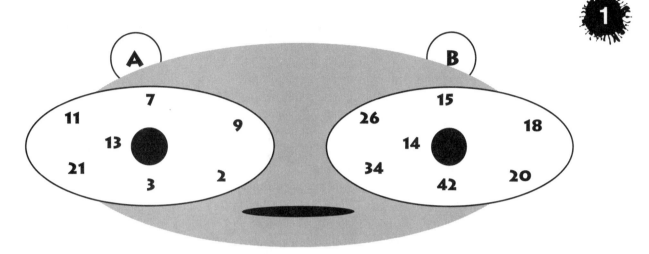

WATCH OUT

2

Look carefully at the sequence of watches and fill in the blank.

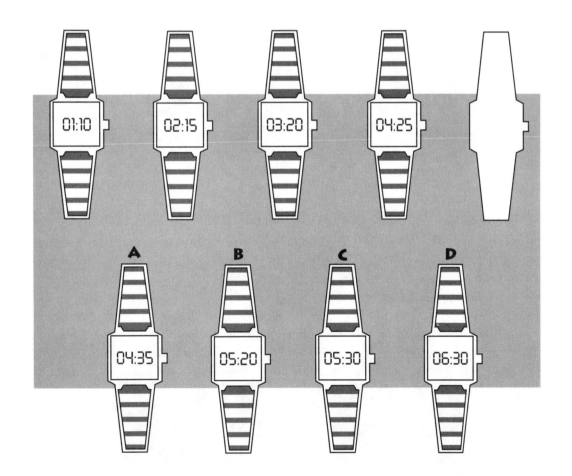

PYRAMID POSER

Work out which number goes at the top of the third pyramid?

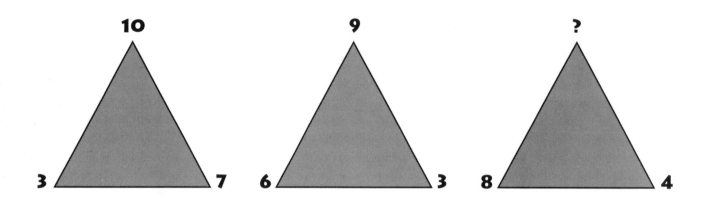

10
3   7

9
6   3

?
8   4

ALL SQUARE

Here is a complete puzzle—work out why it contains these numbers.
(Hint: The center square holds the answer.)

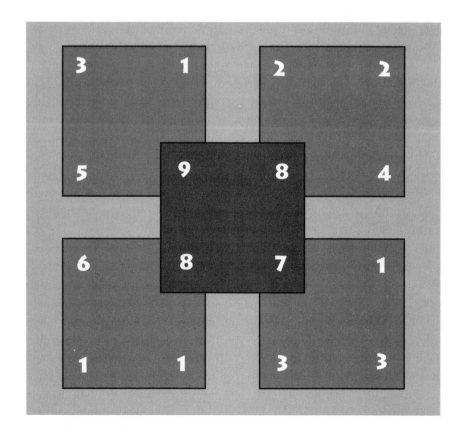

DOMINOES

5

By counting the dots on these dominoes, can you work out
which of the six spare pieces completes the sequence?

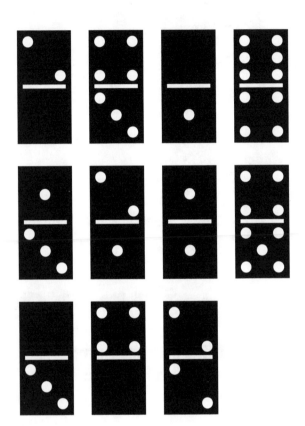

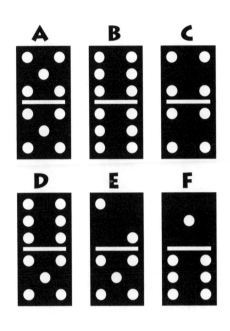

CROSS OVER

6

Which number is missing from each puzzle?

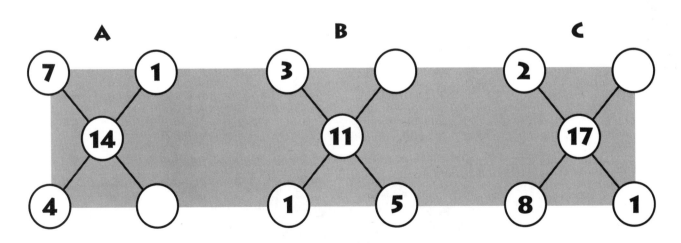

TRI-PIE

Which number is missing from the empty segment?
(Hint: Look at the matching segments on each circle.)

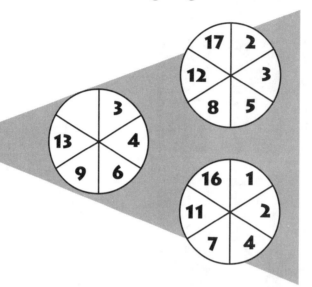

NUMBER BOX

Complete this number box by adding the correct number.
(Hint: The puzzle works up and down as well as side to side!)

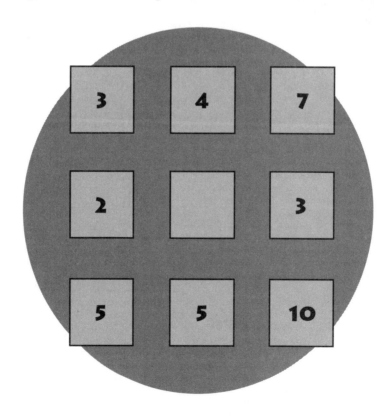

WEB WORLD

9

Which number replaces the question mark and completes the web?
(Hint: Try rotating part of the web.)

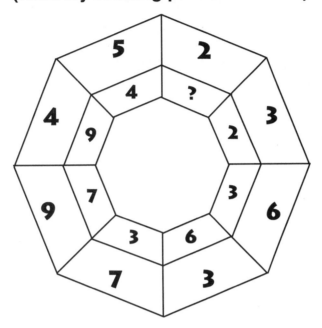

MAGIC SQUARE

10

Fill in the empty circle and complete the puzzle.
(Hint: Look carefully at the grid to find the pattern.)

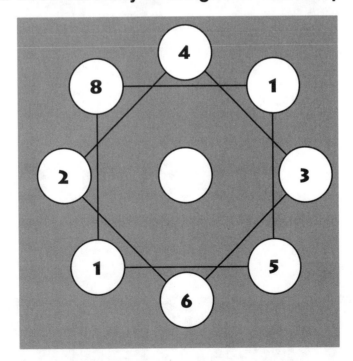

ALL STAR

By using the first two stars as a guide, can you complete this puzzle?

CIRCLES

Which number is needed to finish the puzzle?

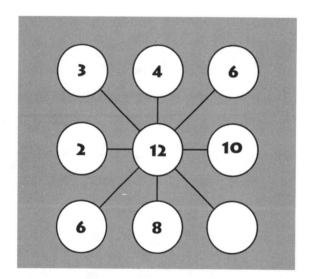

BOXING CLEVER

Which number completes this sequence?

2   3   5   9   ?

MISSING NUMBERS

Which numbers are missing from the empty grid?
(Hint: Look at the matching segments—the middle circle is the link!)

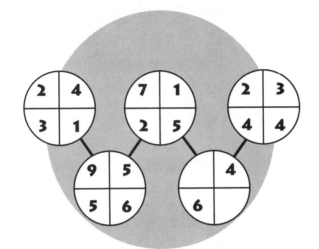

HONEYCOMB

Which number is the odd one out?

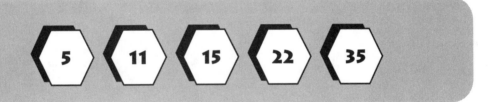

HOLE NUMBERS

Complete this puzzle by adding the correct number to the empty circle.
(Hint: Straight thinking will not help you with this one!)

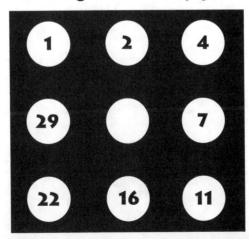

17

FIGURE-IT-OUT

Which three-figure answer is missing from the empty box?

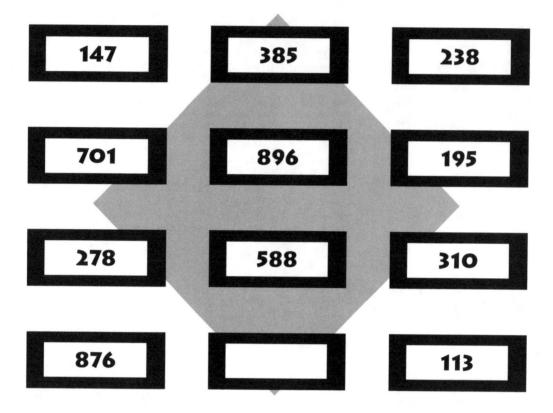

147	385	238
701	896	195
278	588	310
876		113

18

SHAPE UP

Find the missing number to complete the puzzle.

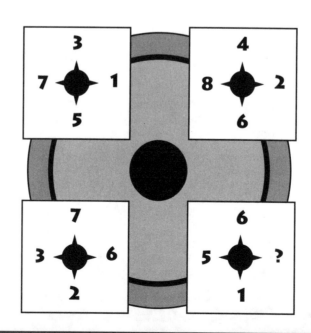

TAKE AWAY

What number goes in the middle oval?
(Hint: It has nothing to do with sums!)

19

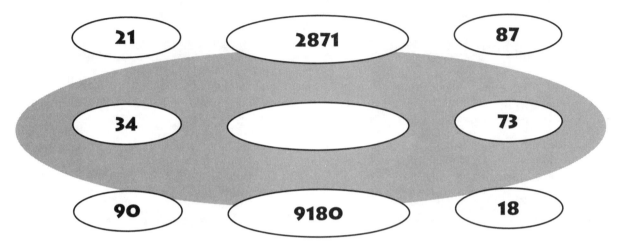

21	2871	87
34		73
90	9180	18

DOTTY!

20

Which of the bottom numbers will go into the center dot?
(Hint: Look at both sides of the grid.)

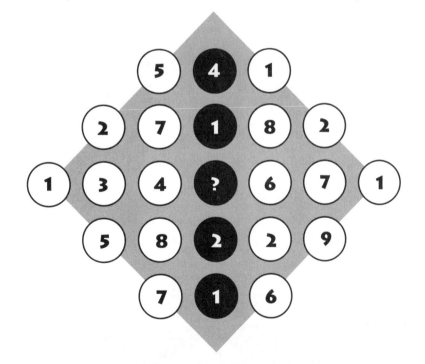

4   5   6   7

ROGUE NUMBER

In each square we have added a rogue number. Can you work out which one it is?

A

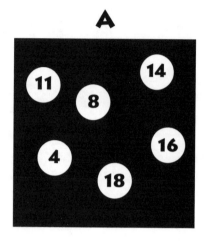

B

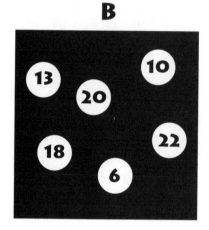

C

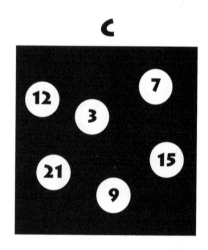

D

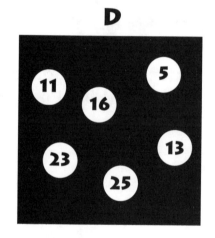

MISSING LINK

Which number completes this chain?

3 5 8 12 17 23 30 ?

LINE UP

23

Using the same rule for every row, can you fill in the empty octagons.

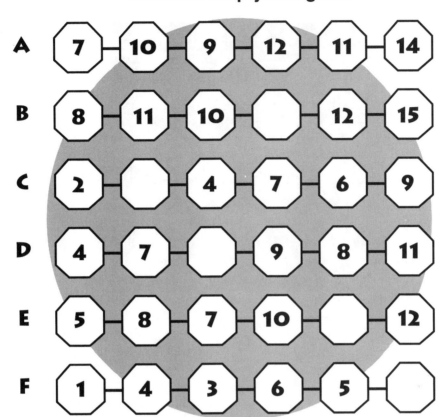

A (7)—(10)—(9)—(12)—(11)—(14)

B (8)—(11)—(10)—(   )—(12)—(15)

C (2)—(   )—(4)—(7)—(6)—(9)

D (4)—(7)—(   )—(9)—(8)—(11)

E (5)—(8)—(7)—(10)—(   )—(12)

F (1)—(4)—(3)—(6)—(5)—(   )

CHANGE IT

24

Replace the question mark with the correct number.
(Hint: Look at the relationship between the numbers in each segment.)

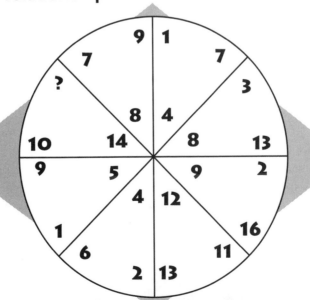

OPTIONS

Which of the three numbers at the bottom will complete this puzzle?
(Hint: Try looking up and down.)

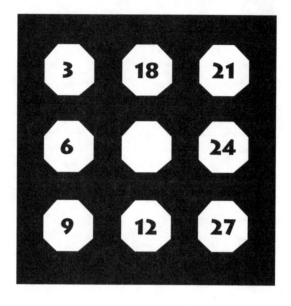

NUMBER SQUARE

By using every number between 2 and 10, can you complete this number
square so that every line, up and down, left to right, and main diagonal,
adds up to 18?

STAR STRUCK

Using the first two stars as an example, find the missing number.

TRIO

Using the first two circles as an example, fill in the empty segment.

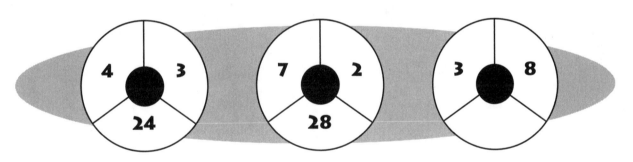

GRID LOCK

Can you work out which numbers are required to complete grids A and B?

6	4	7
1	3	0

2	8	5
7		4

A

3	0	8
5		0

B

1

ODD ONE OUT

Which number is the odd one out in each oval?

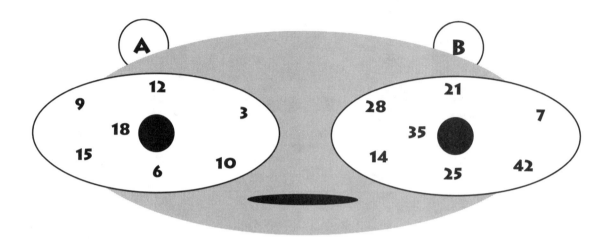

A

12, 9, 3, 18, 15, 6, 10

B

21, 28, 7, 35, 14, 25, 42

2

WATCH OUT

Look carefully at the sequence of watches and fill in the blank.

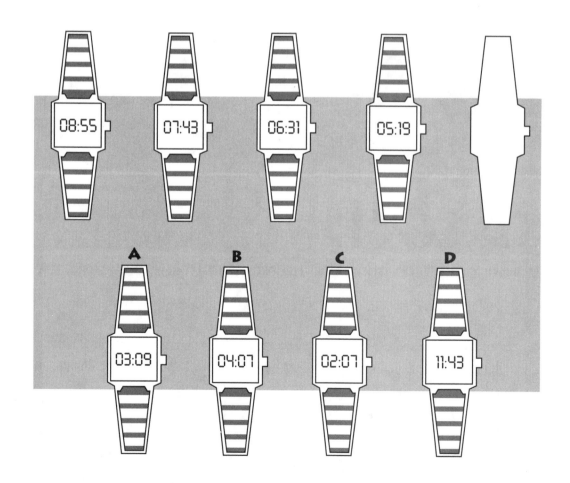

08:55   07:43   06:31   05:19

A 03:09   B 04:07   C 02:07   D 11:43

PYRAMID POSER

Work out which number goes at the top of the third pyramid?

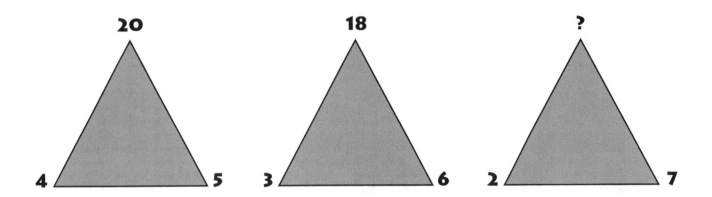

ALL SQUARE

Here is a complete puzzle—work out why it contains these numbers.
(Hint: The center square holds the answer.)

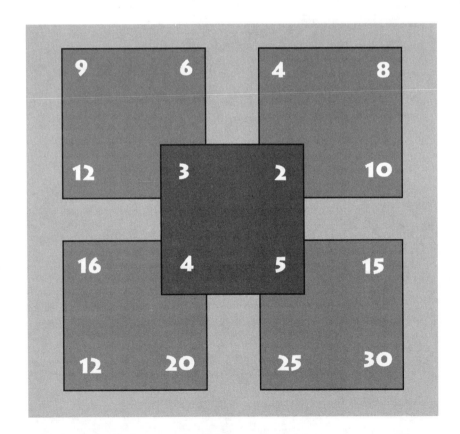

DOMINOES

5

By counting the dots on these dominoes, can you work out
which of the six spare pieces completes the sequence?

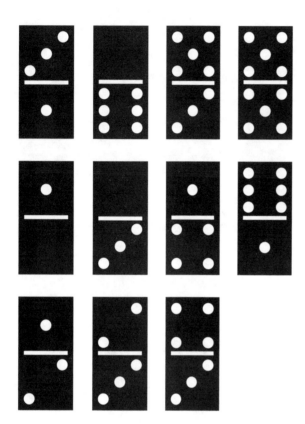

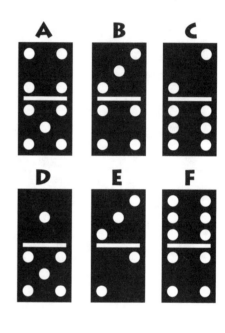

CROSS OVER

6

Which number is missing from each puzzle?

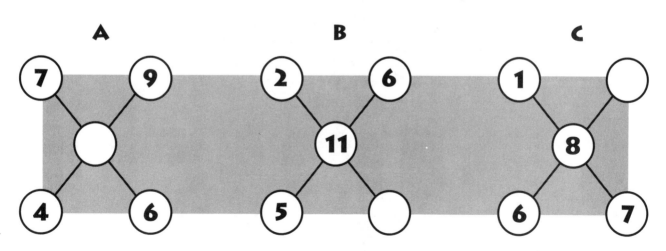

TRI-PIE

Which number is missing from the empty segment?
(Hint: Look at the matching segments on each circle.)

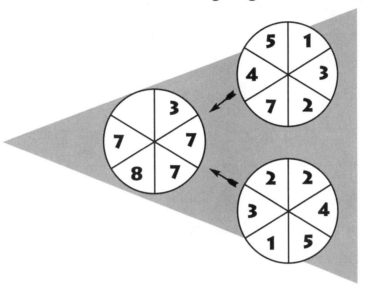

NUMBER BOX

Complete this number box by adding the correct number.
(Hint: The puzzle works up and down as well as side to side!)

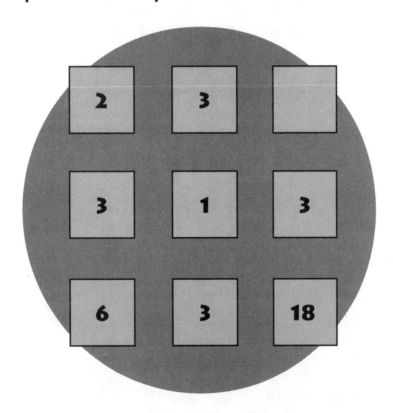

WEB WORLD

Which number replaces the question mark and completes the web?
(Hint: Try rotating part of the web.)

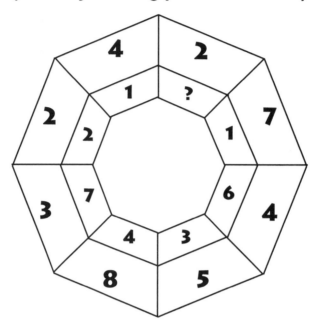

MAGIC SQUARE

Fill in the empty circle and complete the puzzle.
(Hint: Look carefully at the grid to find the pattern.)

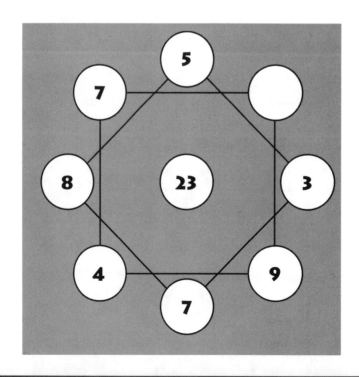

ALL STAR

By using the first two stars as a guide, can you complete this puzzle?
(Hint: Move from point to point).

3   13   4   9   6

7   17   8   13   10

11   21   17   14

CIRCLES

Which number is needed to finish the puzzle?

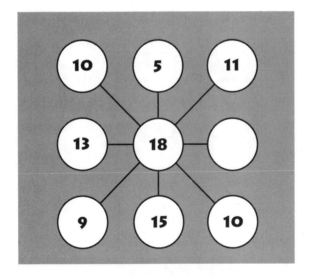

10   5   11

13   18

9   15   10

BOXING CLEVER

Which number completes this sequence?

2   4   10   28   ?

MISSING NUMBERS

Which numbers are missing from the empty grid?
(Hint: Look at the matching segments—the middle circle is the link!)

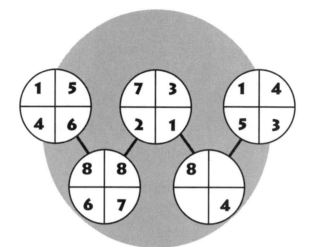

HONEYCOMB

Which number is the odd one out?

HOLE NUMBERS

Complete this puzzle by adding the correct number to the empty circle.
(Hint: Straight thinking will not help you with this one!)

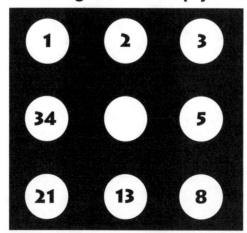

FIGURE-IT-OUT

Which three-figure answer is missing from the empty box?

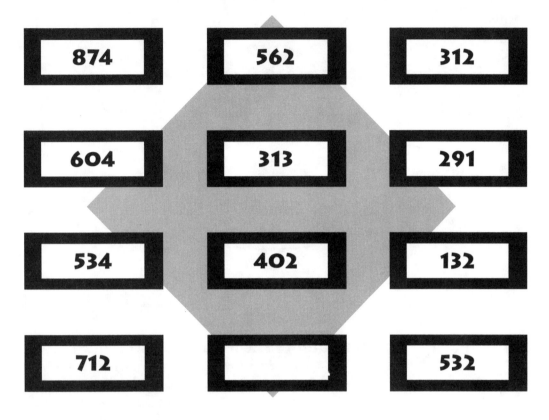

874	562	312
604	313	291
534	402	132
712		532

SHAPE UP

Find the missing number to complete the puzzle.

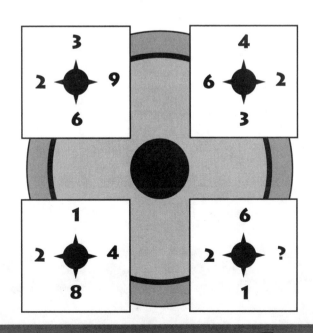

TAKE AWAY

What number goes in the middle oval?
(Hint: It has nothing to do with sums!)

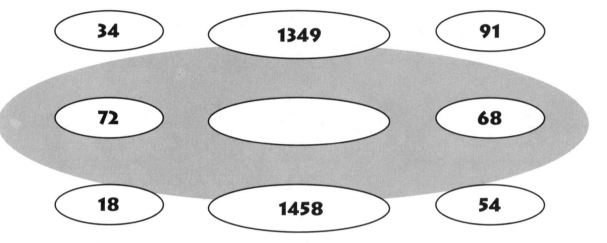

34   1349   91

72   68

18   1458   54

DOTTY!

Which of the bottom numbers will go into the center dot?

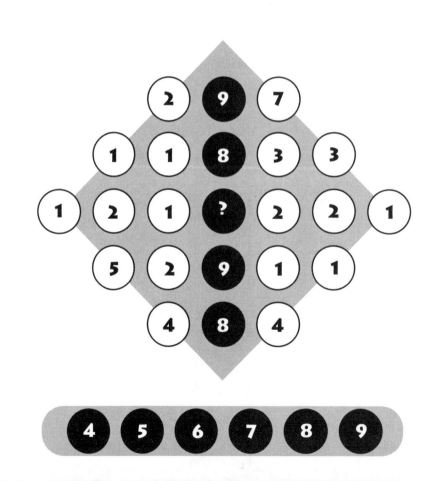

4   5   6   7   8   9

ROGUE NUMBER

In each square we have added a rogue number.
Can you work out which one it is?

21

A

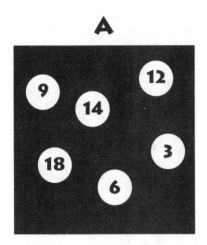

B

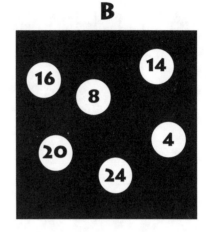

C

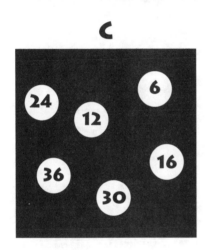

D

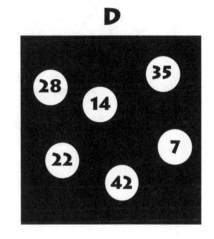

MISSING LINK

22

Which number completes this chain?

3   5   9   15   23   33   45   ?

(23)

LINE UP

Using the same rule for every row, can you
fill in the empty octagons.

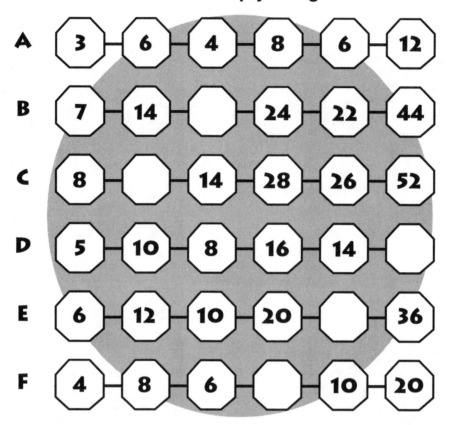

A: 3 — 6 — 4 — 8 — 6 — 12
B: 7 — 14 — ⬡ — 24 — 22 — 44
C: 8 — ⬡ — 14 — 28 — 26 — 52
D: 5 — 10 — 8 — 16 — 14 — ⬡
E: 6 — 12 — 10 — 20 — ⬡ — 36
F: 4 — 8 — 6 — ⬡ — 10 — 20

(24)

CHANGE IT

Replace the question mark with the correct number.
(Hint: Look at the relationship between the numbers in each segment.)

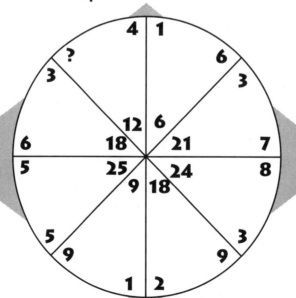

OPTIONS

Which of the three numbers at the bottom will complete this puzzle?
(Hint: Try looking up and down.)

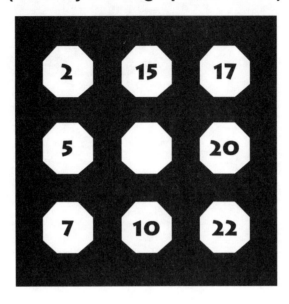

NUMBER SQUARE

By using every number between 1 and 16, can you complete this number square so that every line, up and down, left to right, and main diagonal, adds up to 34?

13			16
	10	11	
	6		
1			4

27 STAR STRUCK

Using the first two stars as an example, find the missing number.

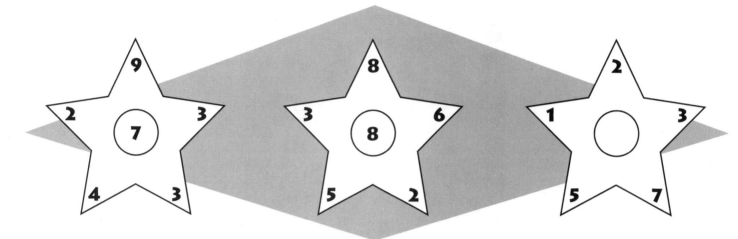

28 TRIO

Using the first two circles as an example, fill in the empty segment.

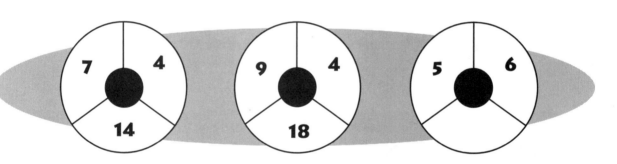

29 GRID LOCK

Can you work out which numbers are required to complete grids A and B?

5	7	8
3	5	6

4	9	8
1		5

A

9	8	7
5		3

B

ODD ONE OUT

Which number is the odd one out in each oval?

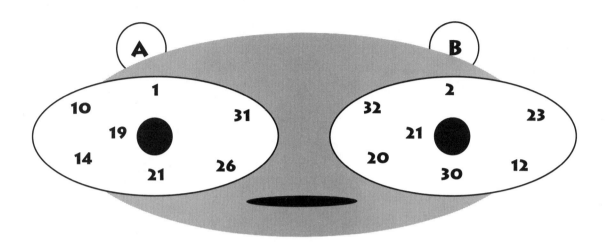

WATCH OUT

Look carefully at the sequence of watches and fill in the blank.

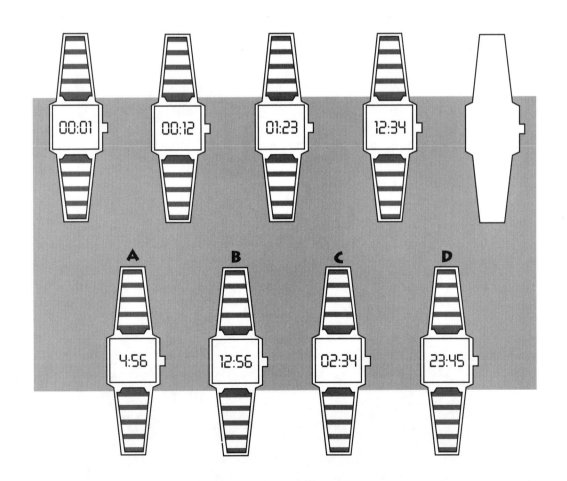

PYRAMID POSER

Work out which number goes at the top of the third pyramid?

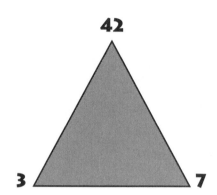

42

3   7

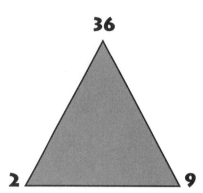

36

2   9

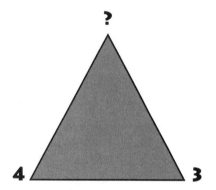

?

4   3

ALL SQUARE

Here is a complete puzzle—work out why it contains these numbers.
(Hint: The center square holds the answer.)

DOMINOES

5

By counting the dots on these dominoes, can you work out
which of the six spare pieces completes the sequence?

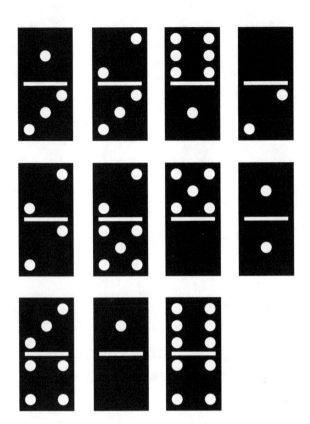

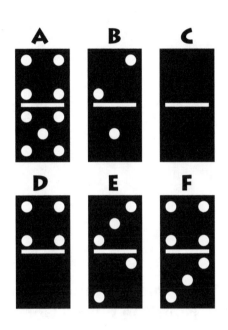

CROSS OVER

6

Which number is missing from each puzzle?

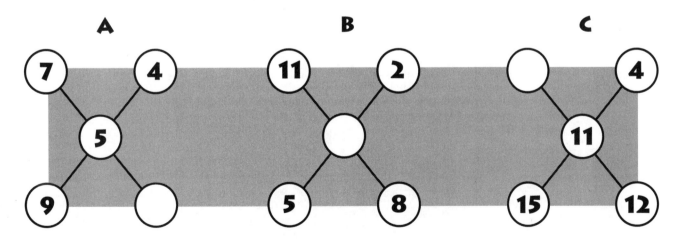

TRI-PIE

Which number is missing from the empty segment?
(Hint: Look at the matching segments on each circle.)

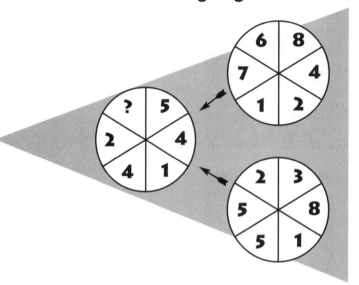

NUMBER BOX

Complete this number box by adding the correct number.
(Hint: The puzzle works up and down as well as side to side!)

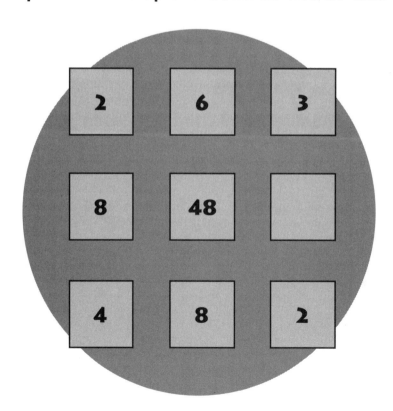

WEB WORLD

Which number replaces the question mark
and completes the web?

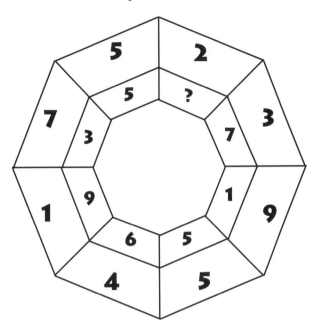

MAGIC SQUARE

Fill in the empty circle and complete the puzzle.
(Hint: Look carefully at the grid to find the pattern.)

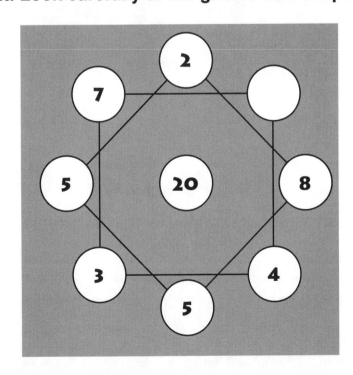

ALL STAR

By using the first two stars as a guide, can you complete this puzzle?

CIRCLES

Which number is needed to finish the puzzle?

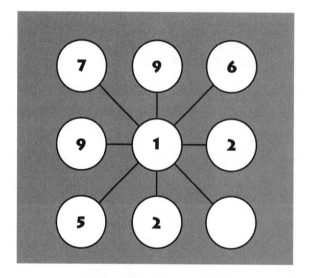

BOXING CLEVER

Which number completes this sequence?

4   5   7   11   ?

MISSING NUMBERS

Which numbers are missing from the empty grid?
(Hint: Look at the matching segments—the middle circle is the link!)

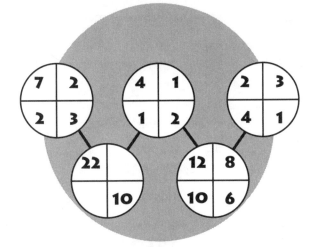

HONEYCOMB

Which number is the odd one out?

HOLE NUMBERS

Complete this puzzle by adding the correct number to the empty circle.
(Hint: Straight thinking will not help you with this one!)

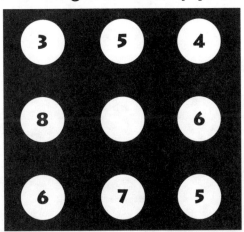

17

FIGURE-IT-OUT

Which four-figure answer is missing from the empty box?

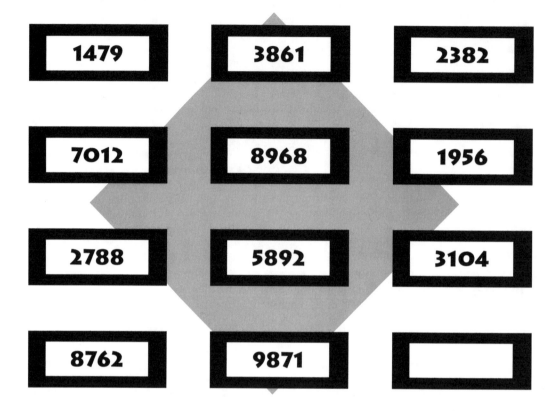

1479	3861	2382
7012	8968	1956
2788	5892	3104
8762	9871	

18

SHAPE UP

Find the missing number to complete the puzzle.

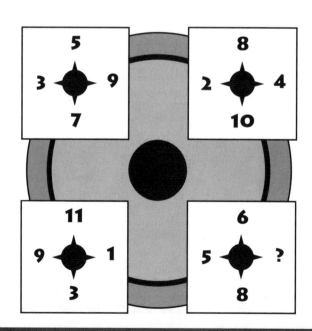

TAKE AWAY

19

What number goes in the middle oval?
(Hint: It has nothing to do with sums!)

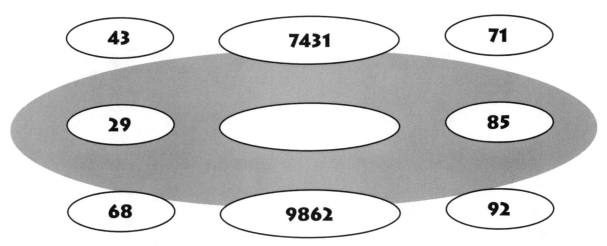

43   7431   71

29   85

68   9862   92

DOTTY!

20

Which of the bottom numbers will go into the center dot?

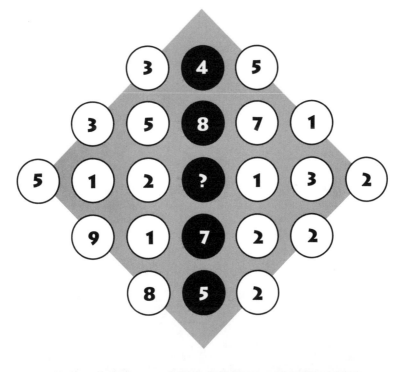

4   5   6   7   8   9

21 ROGUE NUMBER

In each square we have added a rogue number.
Can you work out which one it is?

A

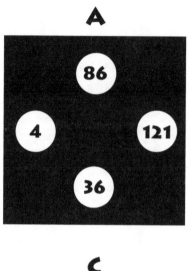

B

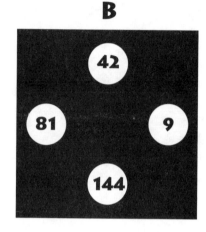

C

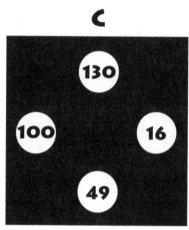

D

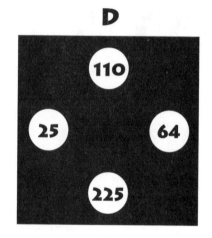

22 MISSING LINK

Which number completes this chain?

LINE UP

23

Using the same rule for every row, can you fill in the empty octagons.

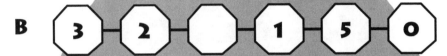

A: 10 — 9 — 11 — 8 — 12 — 7

B: 3 — 2 — ⬡ — 1 — 5 — 0

C: 8 — 7 — 9 — ⬡ — 10 — 5

D: ⬡ — 3 — 5 — 2 — 6 — 1

E: 2 — 1 — 3 — ⬡ — 4 — -1

F: 7 — 6 — ⬡ — 5 — 9 — 4

CHANGE IT

24

Replace the question mark with the correct number.
(Hint: Look at the relationship between the numbers in each segment.)

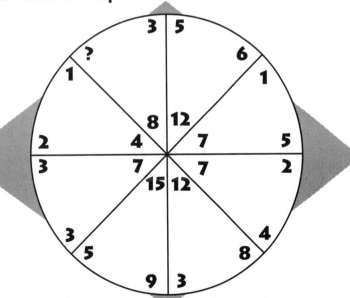

25

OPTIONS

Which of the three numbers at the bottom will complete this puzzle?
(Hint: Try looking up and down.)

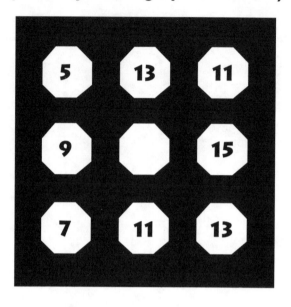

26

NUMBER SQUARE

By using every number between 1 and 16, can you complete this number square so that every line, up and down, left to right, and main diagonal, adds up to 34?

7		9	
		3	
4			11
	15		1

STAR STRUCK

Using the first two stars as an example, find the missing number.

TRIO

Using the first two circles as an example, fill in the empty segment.

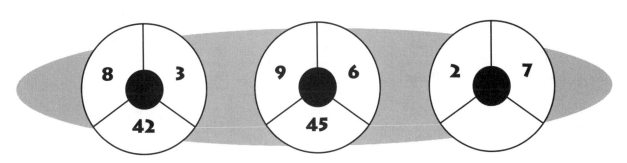

GRID LOCK

Can you work out which numbers are required to complete grids A and B?

2	9	7
4	81	49

6	3	8
36		64

A

1	5	4
1		16

B

1 ODD ONE OUT

Which number is the odd one out in each oval?

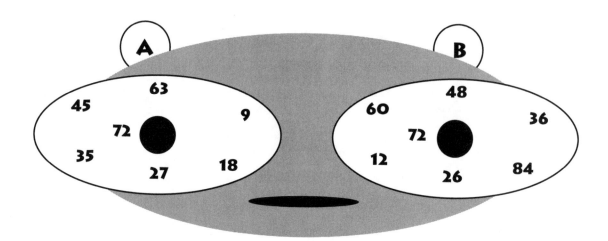

2 WATCH OUT

Look carefully at the sequence of watches and fill in the blank.

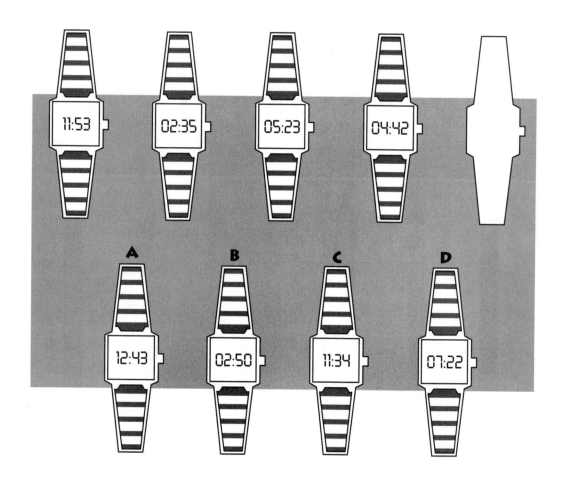

PYRAMID POSER

Work out which number goes at the top of the third pyramid?

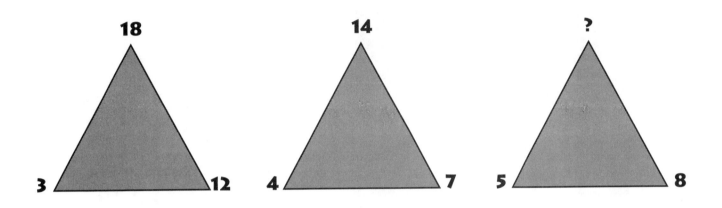

18

3   12

14

4   7

?

5   8

ALL SQUARE

Here is a complete puzzle—work out why it contains these numbers.
(Hint: The center square holds the answer.)

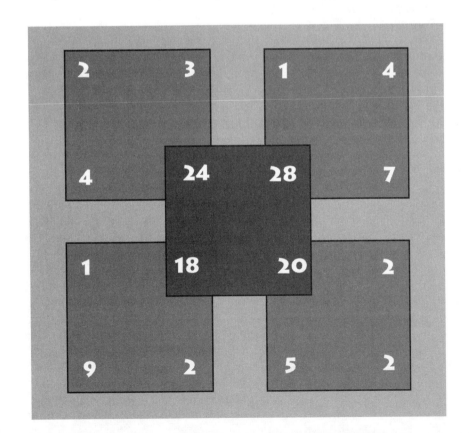

DOMINOES

By counting the dots on these dominoes, can you work out which of the six spare pieces completes the sequence?

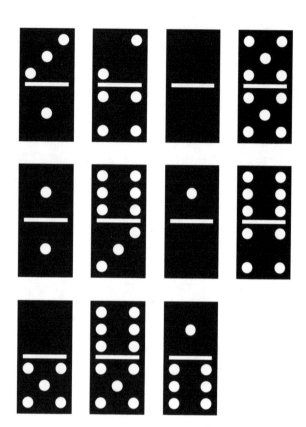

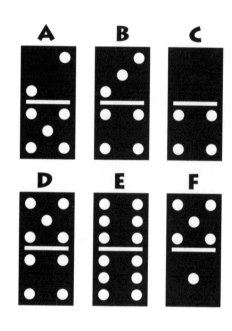

CROSS OVER

Which number is missing from each puzzle?

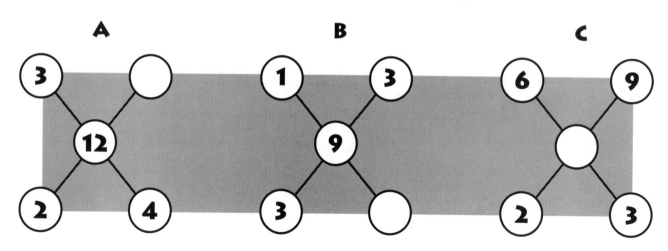

TRI-PIE

Which number is missing from the empty segment?
(Hint: Look at the matching segments on each circle.)

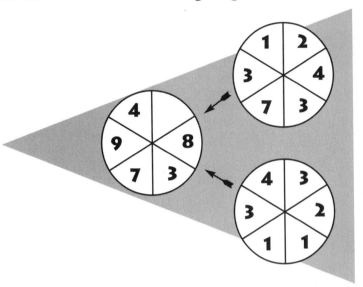

NUMBER BOX

Complete this number box by adding the correct number.
(Hint: The puzzle works up and down as well as side to side!)

WEB WORLD

**Which number replaces the question mark
and completes the web?**

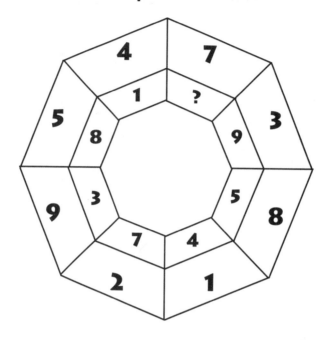

MAGIC SQUARE

**Fill in the empty circle and complete the puzzle.
(Hint: Look carefully at the grid to find the pattern.)**

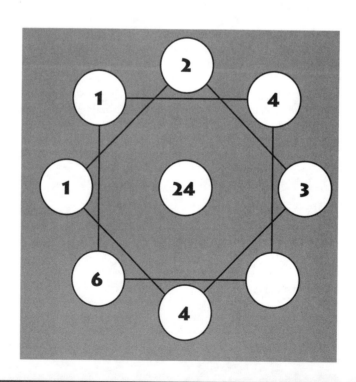

ALL STAR

By using the first two stars as a guide, can you complete this puzzle?

CIRCLES

Which number is needed to finish the puzzle?

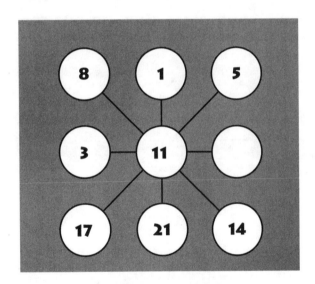

BOXING CLEVER

Which number completes this sequence?

MISSING NUMBERS

Which numbers are missing from the empty grid?
(Hint: Look at the matching segments—the middle circle is the link!)

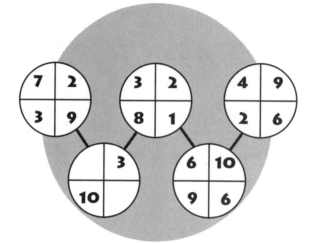

HONEYCOMB

Which number is the odd one out?

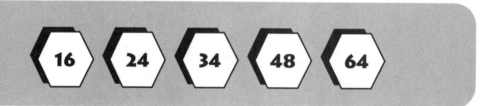

HOLE NUMBERS

Complete this puzzle by adding the correct number to the empty circle.
(Hint: Straight thinking will not help you with this one!)

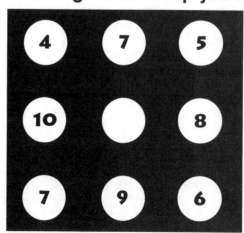

FIGURE-IT-OUT

Which four-figure answer is missing from the empty box?

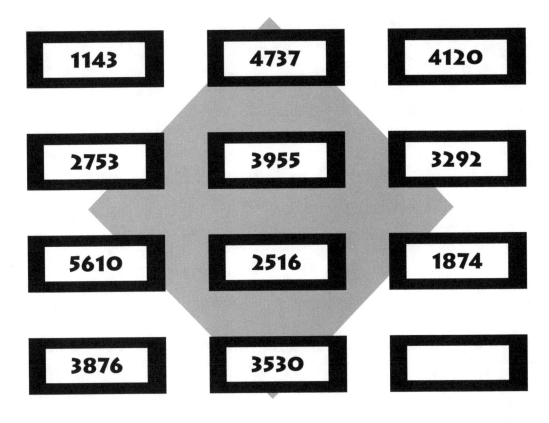

1143	4737	4120
2753	3955	3292
5610	2516	1874
3876	3530	

SHAPE UP

18

Find the missing number to complete the puzzle.

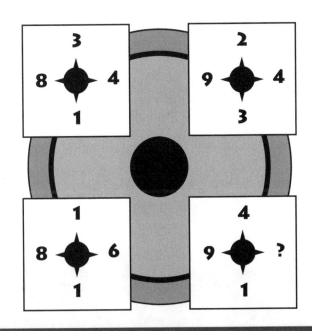

19

TAKE AWAY

What number goes in the middle oval?
(Hint: It has nothing to do with sums!)

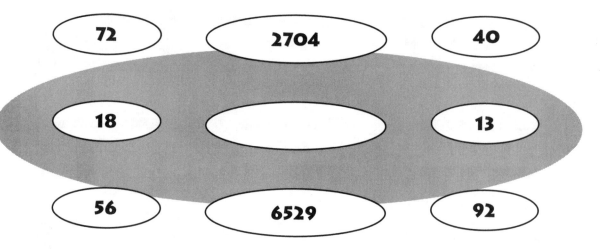

72	2704	40
18		13
56	6529	92

20

DOTTY!

Which of the bottom numbers will go into the center dot?

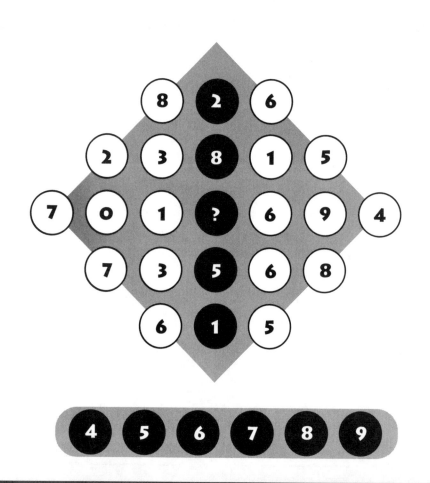

ROGUE NUMBER

In each square we have added a rogue number.
Can you work out which one it is?

A

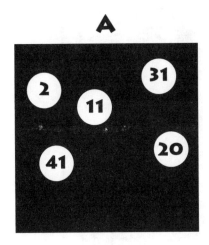

B

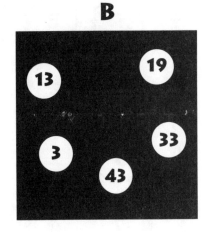

C

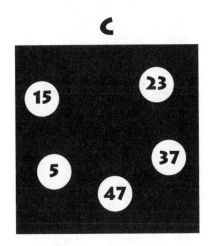

D

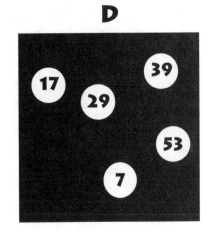

MISSING LINK

Which number completes this chain?

2 10 6 30 26 130 126 ?

23

LINE UP

Using the same rule for every row, can you fill in the empty octagons.

A 9 — 8 — 16 — 13 — 52 — 47

B 4 — 3 — 6 — ( ) — 12 — 7

C 3 — 2 — ( ) — 1 — 4 — -1

D 7 — 6 — 12 — 9 — ( ) — 31

E ( ) — 4 — 8 — 5 — 20 — 15

F 8 — 7 — 14 — ( ) — 44 — 39

24

CHANGE IT

Replace the question mark with the correct number.
(Hint: Look at the relationship between the numbers in each segment.)

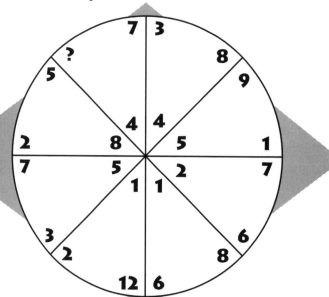

OPTIONS

Which of the three numbers at the bottom will complete this puzzle?
(Hint: Try looking up and down.)

8   34   29

16   ⬡   58

11   22   53

17   28   31

NUMBER SQUARE

By using every number between 1 and 25, can you complete this number square so that every line, up and down, left to right, and main diagonal, adds up to 65?

5			22	25
	18		12	10
23		13		
1	24			21

27

STAR STRUCK

Using the first two stars as an example, find the missing number.

28

TRIO

Using the first two circles as an example, fill in the empty segment.

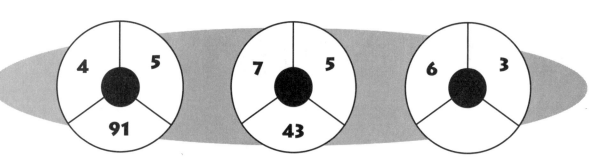

29

GRID LOCK

Can you work out which numbers are required to complete grids A and B?

23	38	16
48	22	16
17	15	14

37	24	16
18	53	17
19		15

A

16	23	12
37	42	16
17		10

B

ODD ONE OUT

Which number is the odd one out in each oval?

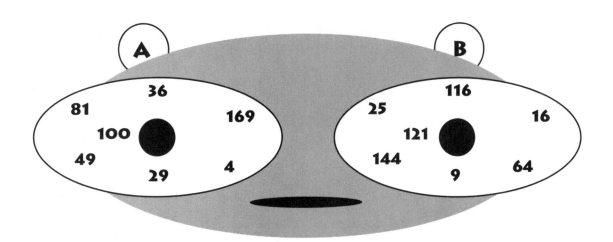

A

36
81   169
100 ●
49   4
29

B

116
25   16
121 ●
144   64
9

WATCH OUT

Look carefully at the sequence of watches and fill in the blank.

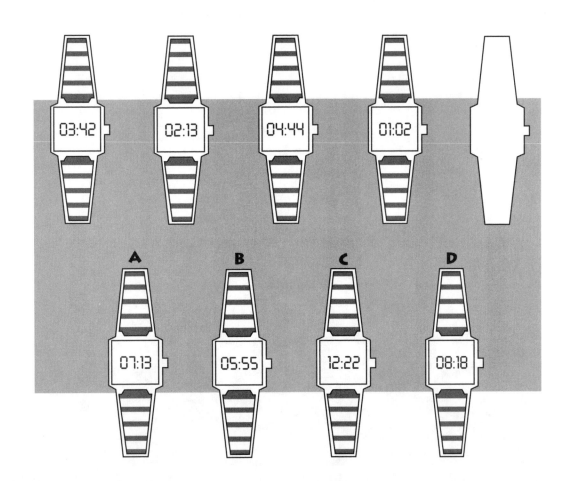

03:42   02:13   04:44   01:02

A   B   C   D
07:13   05:55   12:22   08:18

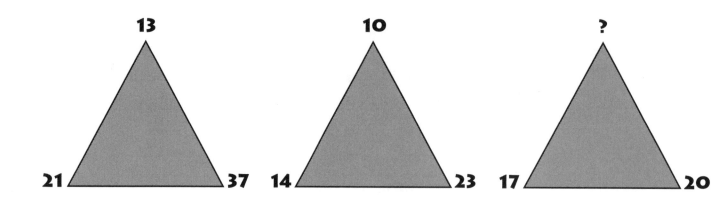

PYRAMID POSER

Work out which number goes at the top of the third pyramid?

13

21 **37**

10

14 **23**

?

17 **20**

ALL SQUARE

Here is a complete puzzle—work out why it contains these numbers.
(Hint: The center square holds the answer.)

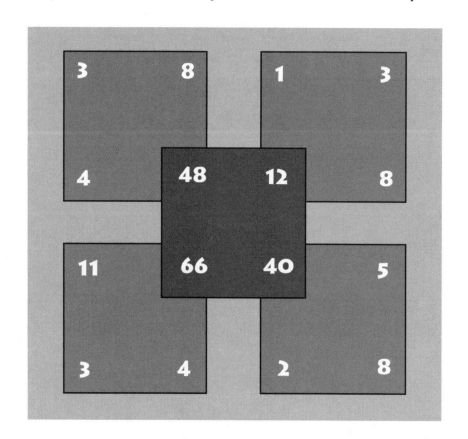

DOMINOES

By counting the dots on these dominoes, can you work out
which of the six spare pieces completes the sequence?

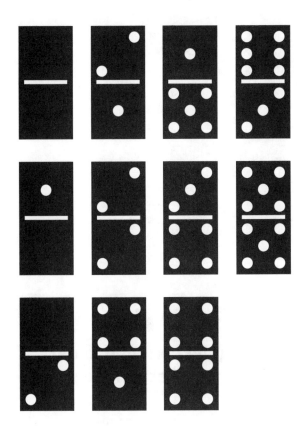

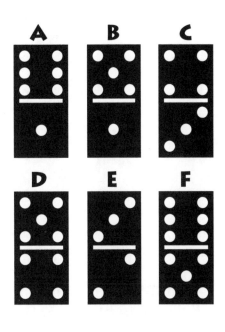

CROSS OVER

Which number is missing from each puzzle?

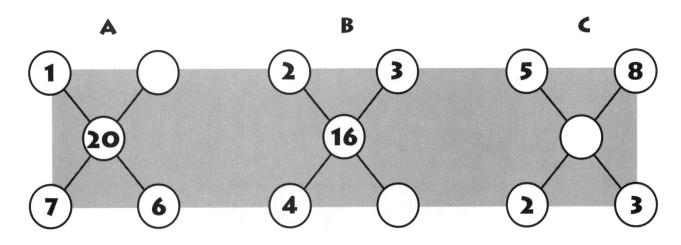

TRI-PIE

Which number is missing from the empty segment?

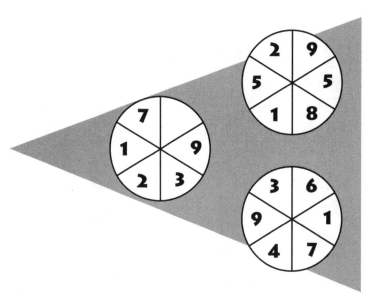

NUMBER BOX

Complete this number box by adding the correct number.
(Hint: The puzzle works up and down as well as side to side!)

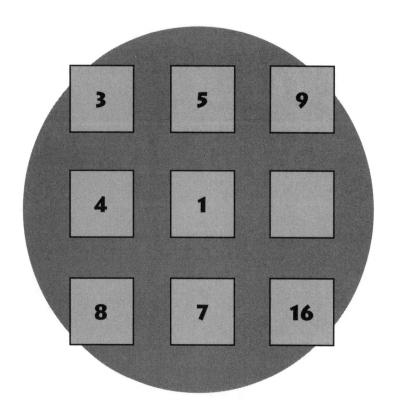

WEB WORLD

9

**Which number replaces the question mark
and completes the web?**

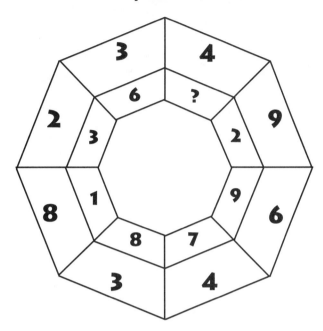

MAGIC SQUARE

10

**Fill in the empty circle and complete the puzzle.
(Hint: Look carefully at the grid to find the pattern.)**

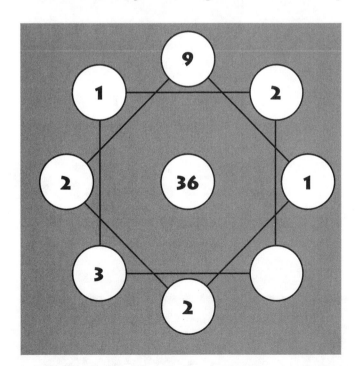

11 ALL STAR

By using the first two stars as a guide, can you complete this puzzle?

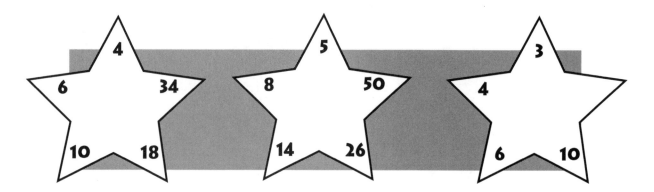

12 CIRCLES

Which number is needed to finish the puzzle?

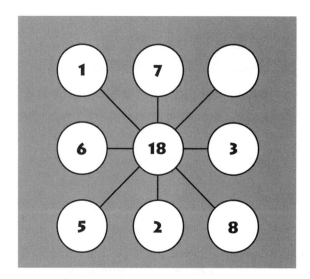

13 BOXING CLEVER

Which number completes this sequence?

| 4 | 9 | 16 | 25 | ? |

MISSING NUMBERS

Which numbers are missing from the empty grid?
(Hint: Look at the matching segments—the middle circle is the link!)

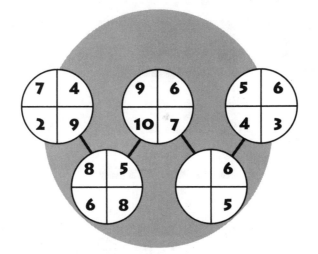

HONEYCOMB

Which number is the odd one out?

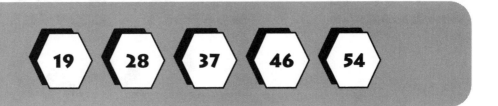

HOLE NUMBERS

Complete this puzzle by adding the correct number to the empty circle.
(Hint: Straight thinking will not help you with this one!)

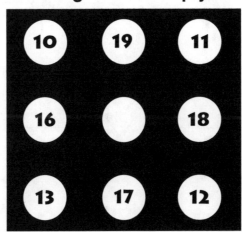

FIGURE-IT-OUT

Which four-figure answer is missing from the empty box?

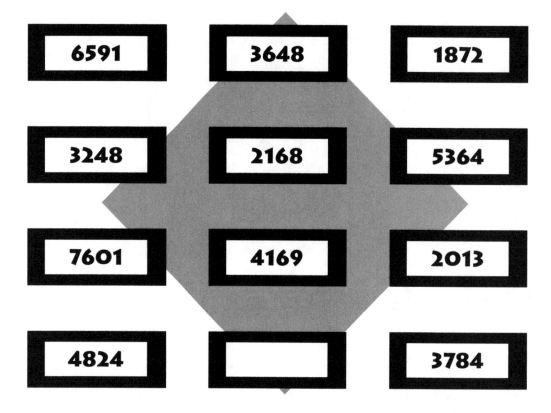

6591 3648 1872

3248 2168 5364

7601 4169 2013

4824 ____ 3784

SHAPE UP

Find the missing number to complete the puzzle.

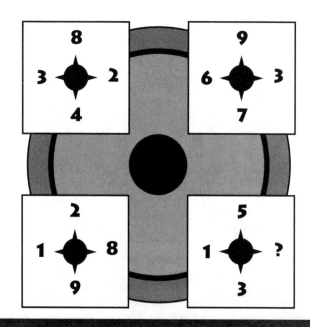

TAKE AWAY

What number goes in the middle oval?
(Hint: It has nothing to do with sums!)

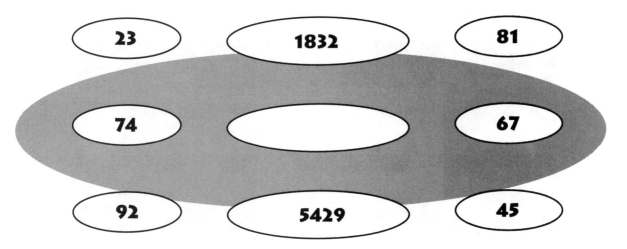

23	1832	81
74		67
92	5429	45

DOTTY!

Which of the bottom numbers will go into the center dot?

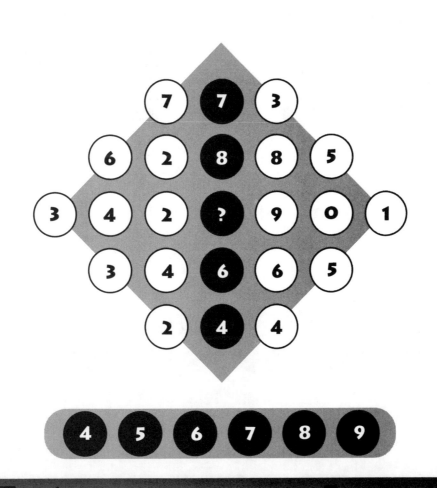

4   5   6   7   8   9

21

ROGUE NUMBER

In each square we have added a rogue number.
Can you work out which one it is?

A

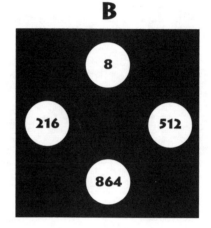
1

125

720

1000

B

8

216

512

864

C

27

324

729

1331

D

64

343

1020

1728

22

MISSING LINK

Which number completes this chain?

 2   10   3   15   8   40   33   ?

LINE UP

Using the same rule for every row, can you
fill in the empty octagons.

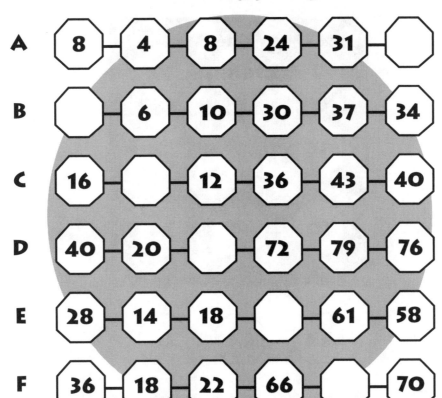

A — 8 — 4 — 8 — 24 — 31 — ◯

B — ◯ — 6 — 10 — 30 — 37 — 34

C — 16 — ◯ — 12 — 36 — 43 — 40

D — 40 — 20 — ◯ — 72 — 79 — 76

E — 28 — 14 — 18 — ◯ — 61 — 58

F — 36 — 18 — 22 — 66 — ◯ — 70

CHANGE IT

Replace the question mark with the correct number.
(Hint: Look at the relationship between the numbers in each segment.)

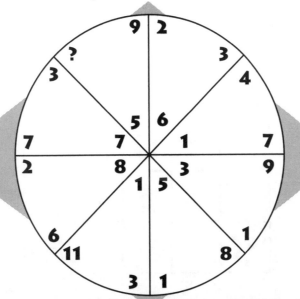

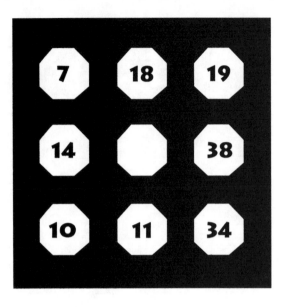

OPTIONS

Which of the three numbers at the bottom will complete this puzzle?
(Hint: Try looking up and down.)

25

7	18	19
14		38
10	11	34

22   24   26

26

NUMBER SQUARE

By using every number between 1 and 25, can you complete this number square so that every line, up and down, left to right, and main diagonal, adds up to 65?

9				15
2			14	
	19	13		1
		6		24
11				

STAR STRUCK

Using the first two stars as an example, find the missing number.

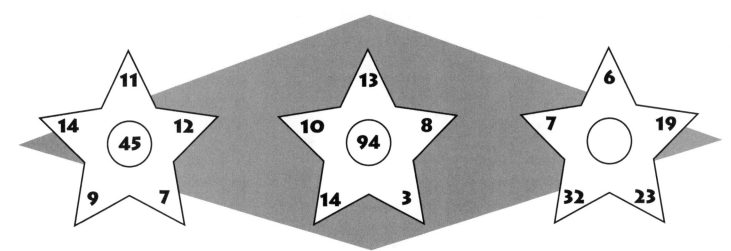

TRIO

Using the first two circles as an example, fill in the empty segment.

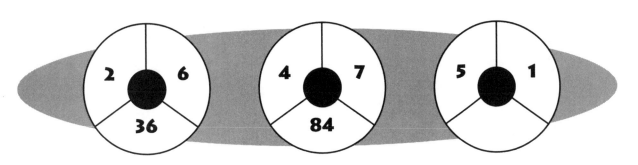

GRID LOCK

Can you work out which numbers are required to complete grids A and B?

38	28	12
57	43	91
32	71	31

24	27	51
43	54	61
31		31

A

17	28	81
59	43	12
22		21

B

TEST 1

1: ODD ONE OUT
Oval A = 2
It is the only even number.
Oval B = 15
It is the only odd number.

2: WATCH OUT
Answer = C
The time increases by 1 hour and 5 minutes each step.

3: PYRAMID POSER
Answer = 12
Add the bottom two numbers together to get the top number.
3 + 7 = 10
6 + 3 = 9
8 + 4 = 12

4: ALL SQUARE
Add the three outer numbers and write the answer in the inner corner.

5: DOMINOES
Answer = D
The dots on the dominoes in the last column equal the total of all the other dots in the same row.

2	4	–		6
–	3	1	=	4

1	2	1		4
3	1	1	=	5

–	4	2		6
3	–	2	=	5

6: CROSS OVER
The middle number in each case is made up of the outer numbers, so that:
A = 2   4 + 7 + 1 + 2 = 14
B = 2   5 + 1 + 3 + 2 = 11
C = 6   1 + 8 + 2 + 6 = 17

7: TRI-PIE
Answer = 18
Moving clockwise around each circle, starting with the lowest number, the numbers increase by 1, then 2, then 3, etc.

8: NUMBER BOX
Answer = 1
Add together the first and second numbers in each line to get the third.
3 + 4 = 7
2 + 1 = 3
5 + 5 = 10

9: WEB WORLD
Answer = 5
The numbers in the inner ring have been moved one place clockwise from the numbers in the outer ring.

10: MAGIC SQUARE
Answer = 15
The four numbers at the corners of the square when added together = 15, and the four numbers that make up the diamond when added together = 15.

11: ALL STAR
Answer = 5
In each star the top number will divide into the other numbers.

12: CIRCLES
Answer = 9
Add together the numbers on the ends of each line to get the middle number.

13: BOXING CLEVER
Answer = 17
Double each number and subtract 1 to get the next.

14: MISSING NUMBERS
Answer = 9 and 9
The numbers in each of the segments in the bottom circles are equal to the sum of the corresponding segments in the connected circles above.
Left and center circles:
2 + 7 = 9
4 + 1 = 5
3 + 2 = 5
1 + 5 = 6
Center and right circles:
7 + 2 = 9
1 + 3 = 4
2 + 4 = 6
5 + 4 = 9

15: HONEYCOMB
Answer = 22
All the other numbers are odd.

16: HOLE NUMBERS
Answer = 37
Starting in the top left corner and moving clockwise in a spiral pattern toward the center, add 1, then 2, then 3, etc.

17: FIGURE IT OUT
Answer = 989
Add the two outer numbers to get the middle number.

18: SHAPE UP
Answer = 2
Add together each pair of opposite numbers to get the same total.

19: TAKE AWAY
Answer = 3734
Put the two digits from the right-hand side in the middle of the two digits from the left-hand side.

20: DOTTY!
Answer = 6
Add together the numbers on the left-hand side of the shaded column, then add together the numbers on the right, and the difference is shown in the center.

21: ROGUE NUMBER
A = 11 The only odd number.
B = 13 The only odd number.
C = 12 The only even number.
D = 16 The only even number.

22: MISSING LINK
Answer = 38
Moving from left to right, add 2, then 3, then 4, etc.

23: LINE UP
Line B = 13
Line C = 5
Line D = 6
Line E = 9
Line F = 8
Moving along the rows, add 3 and then subtract 1 and continue this sequence until the end.

24: CHANGE IT
Answer = 18
The number in the center is midway between the outer two numbers in each segment.

25: OPTIONS
Answer = 15
Moving down the first column, up the second, and down the third, add three each step.

26: NUMBER SQUARE
Numbers in each row add up to 18.

5	10	3
4	6	8
9	2	7

27: STAR STRUCK
Answer = 12
Add up the outer numbers and divide the answer by 2 to get the middle number.

28: TRIO
Answer = 48
Multiply the top two numbers and double the result to get the bottom number.

29: GRID LOCK
Answer: A = 1 and B = 8
Taking each box individually, the sum of the digits in each column are the same in each box.

TEST 2

1: ODD ONE OUT
Oval A = 10
It is the only number not divisible by 3.
Oval B = 25
It is the only number not divisible by 7.

2: WATCH OUT
Answer = B
The time decreases by 1 hour and 12 minutes each step.

3: PYRAMID POSER
Answer = 14
Multiply the bottom two numbers together to get the top number.
4 × 5 = 20
3 × 6 = 18
2 × 7 = 14

4: ALL SQUARE
The outer numbers are all divisible by the inner number.

5: DOMINOES
Answer = A
The total number of dots on each domino increases by 2 each step of the line.

3	–	5	5
1	6	3	5

1	–	1	6
–	3	4	1

1	2	4		4
2	3	3	=	5

6: CROSS OVER
Add together the numbers at each end of the diagonal lines to get the middle number.
A = 13   7 + 6 = 13
         9 + 4 = 13
B = 9   2 + 9 = 11
         6 + 5 = 11
C = 2   1 + 7 = 8
         2 + 6 = 8

7: TRI-PIE
Answer = 7
Add together the matching segments from the two circles on the right and transfer the answer to the corresponding segment in the third circle.

8: NUMBER BOX
Answer = 6
Multiply together the first and second numbers in each line to get the third.
2 × 3 = 6
3 × 1 = 3
6 × 3 = 18

9: WEB WORLD
Answer = 3
The numbers in the inner ring have been moved one place clockwise from the numbers in the outer ring with 1 subtracted.

10: MAGIC SQUARE
Answer = 3
The four numbers at the corners of the square when added together = 23, and the four numbers that make up the diamond when added together also = 23.

11: ALL STAR
Answer = 12
Starting with the top number and moving clockwise add 1 to get the next number, then 2, then 3, etc.

12: CIRCLES
Answer = 7
Add together the numbers on the end of each line and subtract 2 to get the middle number.

13: BOXING CLEVER
Answer = 82
Multiply each number by 3 and subtract 2 to get the next.

14: MISSING NUMBERS
Answer = 7 and 7
The numbers in each of the segments in the bottom circles are equal to the sum of the corresponding segments in the connected circles above.
Left and center circles:
1 + 7 = 8
5 + 3 = 8
4 + 2 = 6
6 + 1 = 7
Center and right circles:
7 + 1 = 8
3 + 4 = 7
2 + 5 = 7
1 + 3 = 4

15: HONEYCOMB
Answer = 23
All the other numbers are even.

16: HOLE NUMBERS
Answer = 55
Starting in the top left corner and moving clockwise in a spiral pattern toward the center, add together the previous two numbers to get the next.

17: FIGURE IT OUT
Answer = 180
Subtract the number in the third column from the number in the first to get the figure in the middle.

18: SHAPE UP
Answer = 3
Multiply each pair of opposite numbers in each box to get the same answer.

19: TAKE AWAY
Answer = 2678
Taking all four digits in the first and last ovals, write them down in numerical order in the middle.

20: DOTTY!
Answer = 9
Add together the numbers on each line and write the answer in the middle column.

21: ROGUE NUMBER
A = 14 All the rest are multiples of 3.
B = 14 All the rest are multiples of 4.
C = 16 All the rest are multiples of 6.
D = 22 All the rest are multiples of 7.

22: MISSING LINK
Answer = 59
Moving from left to right, add an extra 2 each step.

23: LINE UP
Line B = 12
Line C = 16
Line D = 28
Line E = 18
Line F = 12
Moving along the row, multiply by two then subtract two and continue this sequence.

24: CHANGE IT
Answer = 3
Multiply the outer two numbers to get the third.

25: OPTIONS
Answer = 12
Moving down the first column, up the second, and down the third, add three and then two alternately each step.

26: NUMBER SQUARE
Numbers in each row add up to 34.

13	3	2	16
8	10	11	5
12	6	7	9
1	15	14	4

27: STAR STRUCK
Answer = 6
Add up the outer numbers and divide the result by 3 to get the middle numbers.

28: TRIO
Answer = 15
Multiply the top two numbers and divide the result by two to get the bottom number.

29: GRID LOCK
Answer: A = 6 and B = 4
Taking each box individually, the bottom number is three less than the top in grid A and four less in grid B.

TEST 3

1: ODD ONE OUT
Oval A = 26
It is the only number not containing a 1.
Oval B = 30
It is the only number not containing a 2.

2: WATCH OUT
Answer = D
Digits move one place to the left each step.

3: PYRAMID POSER
Answer = 24
Multiply the bottom two numbers and double the result to get the top number.

4: ALL SQUARE
Add the three outer numbers together and divide by three to get the inner number.

5: DOMINOES
Answer = C
Moving along the rows, the dots on all four dominoes add up to 18.

$$\frac{1}{3} + \frac{2}{3} + \frac{6}{1} + \frac{-}{2} = 18$$

$$\frac{2}{2} + \frac{2}{5} + \frac{5}{-} + \frac{1}{1} = 18$$

$$\frac{3}{4} + \frac{1}{-} + \frac{6}{4} + \frac{-}{-} = 18$$

6: CROSS OVER
The middle number in each case is the difference between the numbers on either end of the diagonal lines:
A = 2
B = 3
C = 1

7: TRI-PIE
Answer = 4
The difference between the matching segments from the two circles on the right is written in the corresponding segment in the third circle.

8: NUMBER BOX
Answer = 6
Multiply the first and third numbers in each row and column to get the number in the middle box.

9: WEB WORLD
Answer = 8
Each pair of numbers sums to 10.

10: MAGIC SQUARE
Answer = 6
The four numbers at the corners of the square when added together equal 20, and the four numbers that make up the diamond when added together also equal 20.

11: ALL STAR
Answer = 16
Starting with the top number and moving clockwise, add 2 to get the next number, then subtract 1, add 2 and then finally subtract 1 again.

12: CIRCLES
Answer = 4
Each line of three numbers going through the center circle adds up to 12.

13: BOXING CLEVER
Answer = 19
Multiply each number by 2 and then subtract 3 to get the next number.

14: MISSING NUMBERS
Answer = 6 and 6
The numbers in each of the segments in the bottom circles are equal to double the numbers in the matching segments of the connected circles above.
Left and center circles:
7 + 4 = 11 (22)
2 + 1 = 3 (6)
2 + 1 = 3 (6)
3 + 2 = 5 (10)
Center and right circles:
4 + 2 = 6 (12)
3 + 1 = 4 (8)
1 + 4 = 5 (10)
2 + 1 = 3 (6)

15: HONEYCOMB
Answer = 20
All the other numbers are multiples of three.

16: HOLE NUMBERS
Answer = 7
Starting in the top left corner and moving clockwise in a spiral pattern toward the center, add 2 for the next number, subtract 1 for the next, add 2, subtract 1, etc.

17: FIGURE IT OUT
Answer = 1109
Add together the numbers in the first and third columns to get the number in the middle.

18: SHAPE UP
Answer = 5
The sum of the numbers in each square is 24.

19: TAKE AWAY
Answer = 9852
Take all four digits shown in each line and write them in reverse numerical order in the middle.

20: DOTTY!
Answer = 7
Add together the numbers in each row and divide the result by 2 to get the middle number.

21: ROGUE NUMBER
A = 86, B = 42, C = 130, D = 110
All the others are square numbers. (2 × 2 = 4, 3 × 3 = 6, 4 × 4 = 16, etc.)

22: MISSING LINK
Answer = 10
Moving from left to right, add 2 for the next number, then subtract 1 for the next, and continue this sequence.

23: LINE UP
Line B = 4
Line C = 6
Line D = 4
Line E = 0
Line F = 8
Moving along the rows, subtract 1, add 2, subtract 3, add 4, and then subtract 5.

24: CHANGE IT
Answer = 4
Add together the two outer numbers in each segment and add 1 to get the number in the middle.

25: OPTIONS
Answer = 9
Moving down the first column, up the second, and down the third, add 4 and then subtract 2 alternately each step.

26: NUMBER SQUARE
Numbers in each row add up to 34.

7	2	9	16
13	12	3	6
4	5	14	11
10	15	8	1

27: STAR STRUCK
Answer = 10
Add up the outer numbers, divide by 2, and then add 3 to get the middle numbers.

28: TRIO
Answer = 41
Multiply the top two numbers and write the answer in reverse at the bottom.

29: GRID LOCK
Answer: A = 9 and B = 25
Square the top number in each box to get the bottom number.
(3 × 3 = 9, 5 × 5 = 25)

TEST 4

1: ODD ONE OUT
Oval A = 35
It is the only number not divisible by 9.
Oval B = 26
It is the only number not divisible by 12.

2: WATCH OUT
Answer = A
The digits shown on each watch add up to 10 every time.

3: PYRAMID POSER
Answer = 20
Multiply the bottom two numbers together and divide the result by 2 to get the top number.
3 × 12 = 36 (18)
4 × 7 = 28 (14)
5 × 8 = 40 (20)

4: ALL SQUARE
Multiply the three outer numbers together to get the number in the middle.

5: DOMINOES
Answer = D
Moving along the lines, add the dots of the first two dominoes together and then subtract the dots from the third to get the answer shown in the last column.

3		2		–		5
1	+	4	–	–	=	5

1		6		1		6
1	+	3	–	–	=	4

–		6		1		5
5	+	5	–	6	=	4

6: CROSS OVER
Multiply the numbers at each end of the diagonal lines to get the middle number.
A = 6
B = 9
C = 18

7: TRI-PIE
Answer = 6
Multiply the matching segments from the two circles on the right and transfer the answer to the corresponding segment in the third circle.

8: NUMBER BOX
Answer = 14
Multiply together the first and second numbers in each line and then divide the result by 2 to get the number in the third box.

9: WEB WORLD
Answer = 2
The numbers in the inner ring match those of the outer ring in the opposite segment.

10: MAGIC SQUARE
Answer = 1
The four numbers at the corners of the square when multiplied together = 24, and the four numbers that make up the diamond when multiplied together = 24.

11: ALL STAR
Answer = 5
Starting with the top number and moving clockwise, double each number and subtract 1 to get the next.

12: CIRCLES
Answer = 19
The middle number is midway between the other two numbers on each line.

13: BOXING CLEVER
Answer = 106
Add three to each number and double the result to get the next.

14: MISSING NUMBERS
Answer = 9 and 9
The numbers in each of the segments in the bottom circles are equal to the sum, minus 1, of the corresponding segments in the connected circles above.
Left and center circles:
7 + 3 – 1 = 9
2 + 2 – 1 = 3
3 + 8 – 1 = 10
9 + 1 – 1 = 9
Center and right circles:
3 + 4 – 1 = 6
2 + 9 – 1 = 10
8 + 2 – 1 = 9
1 + 6 – 1 = 6

15: HONEYCOMB
Answer = 34
All the other numbers are multiples of 8.

16: HOLE NUMBERS
Answer = 8
Starting in the top left corner and moving clockwise in a spiral pattern toward the center, add 3 for the next number, subtract 2, and continue this sequence.

17: FIGURE IT OUT
Answer = 2594
The three numbers in each row add up to 10,000.

18: SHAPE UP
Answer = 4
Add together the top and bottom numbers. Subtract the right-hand number from the left. The answer is always the same.

19: TAKE AWAY
Answer = 8131
Reverse the digits shown in the small ovals (left then right) and write the figure in the middle.

20: DOTTY!
Answer = 7
Taking the number shown on each side as a whole number, subtract the right-hand side from the left-hand side.
(701 – 694 = 7)

21: ROGUE NUMBER
A = 20, B = 33, C = 15, D = 39
All the rest are prime numbers. (Numbers that are only divisible by themselves and 1.)

22: MISSING LINK
Answer = 630
Moving from left to right, multiply by 5 for the next number, subtract 4 for the next, and continue this sequence.

23: LINE UP
Line A = 3
Line B = 3
Line C = 4
Line D = 36
Line E = 5
Line F = 11
Moving along the row, subtract 1, multiply by 2, subtract 3, multiply by 4, and then subtract 5.

24: CHANGE IT
Answer = 4
The numbers in each segment add up to 15.

25: OPTIONS
Answer = 17
Moving down the first column, up the second, and down the third, double the first number to get the second, then subtract 5 for the third, and continue this sequence.

26: NUMBER SQUARE
Numbers in each row add up to 65.

5	2	11	22	25
16	18	9	12	10
23	7	13	19	3
20	14	17	8	6
1	24	15	4	21

27: STAR STRUCK
Answer = 36
Add up the outer numbers and write the answer in reverse in the middle.

28: TRIO
Answer = 71
Multiply the top two numbers, subtract 1, and write the answer in reverse in the bottom segment.

29: GRID LOCK
Answer: A = 14 and B = 11
The numbers in the third boxes in each row and column are the sum of the digits in the first two boxes.

TEST 5

1: ODD ONE OUT
A = 29, B = 116
All other numbers are square numbers.

2: WATCH OUT
Answer = B
The sum of the digits shown on the minutes side equal double the sum of the digits shown on the hour side.

3: PYRAMID POSER
Answer = 10
Add the bottom digits together to get the top number.
2 + 1 + 3 + 7 = 13
1 + 4 + 2 + 3 = 10
1 + 7 + 2 + 0 = 10

4: ALL SQUARE
Multiply the outer three numbers and divide by 2 to get the inner number.

5: DOMINOES
Answer = F
Moving along the lines, the dots on each domino increase by three each step.

–	2	1	6
–	1	5	3

1	2	3	5
–	2	4	5

–	4	4	6
2	1	4	5

6: CROSS OVER
Multiply the numbers on each end of the diagonal lines and add each answer together to get the middle number.
A = 2, B = 2, C = 31

7: TRI-PIE
Answer = 8
Each pair of opposite numbers equals 10.

8: NUMBER BOX
Answer = 6
Add up the first two numbers in each row and column and then add 1 to get the last number.

9: WEB WORLD
Answer = 5
The numbers in each of the four opposite segments (inner and outer rings) add up to 20.

10: MAGIC SQUARE
Answer = 6
Multiply the four numbers that make up the square to get the same answer you do when multiplying the four numbers that make up the diamond.

11: ALL STAR
Answer = 18
Starting with the top number and moving counterclockwise, double each number and subtract 2 to get the next number.

12: CIRCLES
Answer = 4
Add together the numbers on the end of each line and double the result to get the middle number.

13: BOXING CLEVER
Answer = 36
The numbers will be the first five square numbers.
(2 × 2 = 4, 3 × 3 = 9,
4 × 4 = 16, 5 × 5 = 25, and
6 × 6 = 36)

14: MISSING NUMBERS
Answer = 7 and 7
The numbers in each of the segments in the bottom circles are equal to half the sum of the matching segments in the connected circles above.
Left and center circles:
7 + 9 = 16 (8)
4 + 6 = 10 (5)
2 + 10 = 12 (6)
9 + 7 = 16 (8)
Center and right circles:
9 + 5 = 14 (7)
6 + 6 = 12 (6)
10 + 4 = 14 (7)
7 + 3 = 10 (5)

15: HONEYCOMB
Answer = 54
The digits shown in the other numbers always add up to 10.

16: HOLE NUMBERS
Answer = 14
Starting in the top left corner and moving clockwise in a spiral pattern toward the center, add 9, subtract 8, add 7, subtract 6, etc.

17: FIGURE IT OUT
Answer = 8068
Add together the numbers in the first and third columns and write the answer in reverse in the middle column.

18: SHAPE UP
Answer = 5
Multiply the top and bottom numbers and write the answer as single digits on the left and right.

19: TAKE AWAY
Answer = 7647
Taking all four digits shown in the first and last ovals, write this figure down in reverse in the middle.

20: DOTTY!

Answer = 9

The figure in the middle column is the same as the highest number in each row.

21: ROGUE NUMBER

A = 720, B = 864, C = 324, D = 1020

All other numbers are cube numbers (2 × 2 × 2 = 8, 3 × 3 × 3 = 27, etc.)

22: MISSING LINK

Answer = 165

Moving from left to right, multiply by 5 for the next number, then subtract 7 for the next, and continue this sequence.

23: LINE UP

Line A = 28
Line B = 12
Line C =   8
Line D = 24
Line E = 54
Line F = 73

Moving along the rows, divide by 2, add 4, multiply by 3, add 7, and subtract 3.

24: CHANGE IT

Answer = 4

The total of the numbers in each segment increases by 1 moving clockwise around the circle.

25: OPTIONS

Answer = 22

Moving down the first column, up the second, and down the third, double the first number to get the next, subtract 4 for the next, and then add 1. Continue this sequence until the end.

26: NUMBER SQUARE

Numbers in each row add up to 65.

9	3	22	16	15
2	21	20	14	8
25	19	13	7	1
18	12	6	5	24
11	10	4	23	17

27: STAR STRUCK

Answer = 88

Add up the outer numbers, add 1, and then write the answer in reverse in the middle.

28: TRIO

Answer = 15

Multiply the top two numbers and triple the result to get the bottom number.

29: GRID LOCK

Answer: A = 81 and B = 71

The numbers in the third boxes in each row and column are the sum of the digits in the first two boxes in reverse.